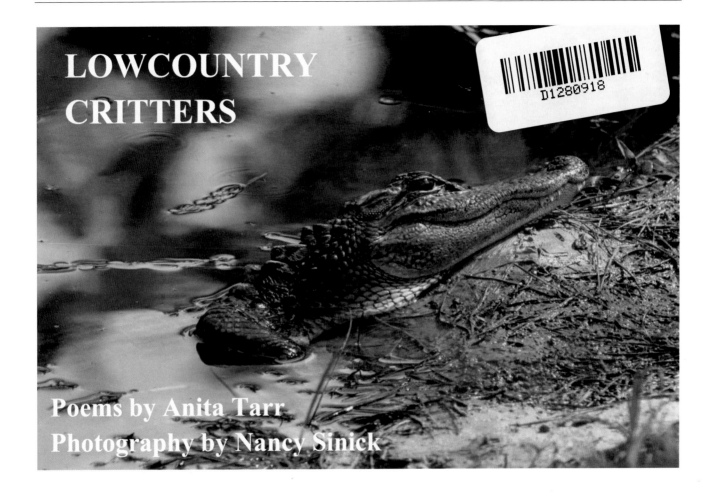

LOWCOUNTRY CRITTERS

Poems by Anita Tarr
Photography by Nancy Sinick

Great Blue Heron

Great Blue Heron,
still and silent as the moon,
eye peeled for that sucker fish
to flash between her clawed feet.

Her beak flashes.
     She rises,
wings beating against the air,
meal trailing from her mouth.

Great Blue Heron

     Flying, then,
casting a shadow over you
big as a Pterodactyl's.

Which came first—
The *wood stork* or Gru?
The long stick legs,
the hulking chest,
the pointy beak,
the hunched shoulders—
each is a silhouette of the other.

But one has minions;
the other has friends.

One is despicable—
or does he pretend?

Wood Stork

One wants
to steal the moon
from the night,
to rob from us
our cheering light.

The other simply
wants to fly
and catch the winds
across the sky.

Not so long ago
and not so very far away,
  snowy *egrets* were hunted
  almost to extinction.
Their showy white plumes
  adorned ladies' hats.

Theirs was a fatal beauty.

Now, egrets fly free.

Their feathery white plumes
adorn only themselves
as they roost in the trees
and care for their young.

The *anhinga* is spreading his wings to dry.
Such an ordinary thing.
So why does he look so glorious?

Cardinals, blackbirds,
bluebirds, sparrows,
robin redbreasts,
Carolina wrens—
the singers, males,
with full-throated ease
release their varied melodies.

But *mockingbirds*—
they mimic best
the songs they hear
from all the rest.

The *osprey* perches
  atop a dying tree.
His beak and claws
  are sharp and curved.
His flight is
  straight and true.

Osprey

He swoops
over water
and scoops up
a fish,
carries it back
in his claws
to his nest,
where gaping
mouths await,
impatiently.

Black Vulture

The *buzzard* steps an awkward gait
    like a woman wearing a bustle.
But when he flies he mystifies
    with his airborne shuffle.
Round and round a circle he soars,
    eyeing his treat on the ground.
The treat can't see him, nor can feel him
    biting and swallowing him down.

Monarchs

Egg.
Caterpillar.
Chrysalis.
Adult.

Four ways of being.

Each one,
different.

Each one,
the same butterfly.

How can this be?

A tiny *egg*

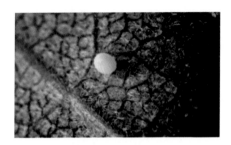

becomes a hungry *caterpillar*,
eating and eating and eating,

until it becomes a *chrysalis,*
    bejeweled,
      so fragile and still,
but inside it's turning
    and churning
    and yearning
      to break free—

to become a *butterfly*.

Lowcountry Vampires

So small you can't see them
  are *no-see-ums*.
They come for you in a cloud,
  and stay until they're full.

The *tick* gorges on your blood
  without you even knowing.
She takes your blood, and leaves behind
  a little gift that itches.

The *mosquito* is a dainty creature,
  sprightly legs splayed out from that tiny body.
You can't see her red mouth
  dripping from her last victim.

A palmetto bug by any other name
   smells just as bad.
Glossy black, its broad back big enough
   for an elfin rider.

It scuttles back into darkness,
      away from your shoe.

This mound of sand spells out DON'T TREAD ON ME!   Step on it,
and a mass of miniscule mandibles will carve out tiny fire pits in your legs.
They are unforgiving, these *fire ants*.

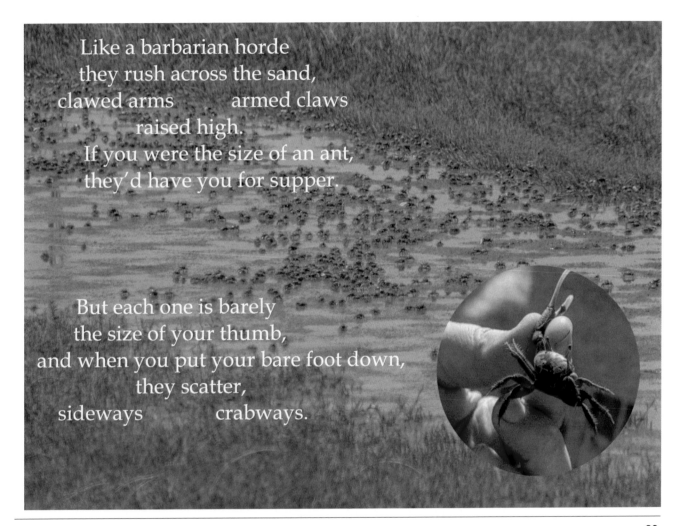

Like a barbarian horde
    they rush across the sand,
clawed arms   armed claws
            raised high.
    If you were the size of an ant,
    they'd have you for supper.

    But each one is barely
    the size of your thumb,
and when you put your bare foot down,
            they scatter,
    sideways   crabways.

The tiny *tree frog* folds her limbs
into an oval of green,
her feet sticking to the wall.

Then—

WHISH!   She explodes—

leaping through the air,
soaring to the floor,
the chair,
your hair.

Does she have a target?

Or does she just leap to   who
knows
where?

The *copperhead* drapes himself across the gravel path, the rocks still warm from the sun. Exposed, he slithers into leaf mold and pine straw. His rust and brown markings work well here. His cat eyes are open to the world.

He can feel you coming. But he does not move. Wherever he is, is his space. Even Jack couldn't jump over this poisonous stick.
Back away!   Back away.

A turtle naps upon a rock, grey upon grey, an outgrowth, a shadowy hump. Nearby sprawls an alligator—with jaws that bite and claws that catch!— still as stone.

His massive tail can flip a boat. His leather armor's tough and scaly.
His sharp teeth (the better to eat you with, my dear) can rip off an arm
and swallow it whole. In winter he bromates for months,
not eating, barely breathing, at the bottom of the water.

Alligators just like this one shared the earth with dinosaurs.
He hasn't changed for millions of years.
Why should he, when he is perfect?

All you can see on the water are

TWO   EYES

and a

S

N

O

U

T

Mother *alligator* builds her nest in the woods by the water, a large mound of sticks and dirt and leaves. She lays her eggs there, fifty or so, and waits. When they begin to hatch two months later, she is still there. They chirp, chirp, chirp, and she comes running to help.

She carries the hatchlings in her toothy mouth to the water.
She hauls them on her back across the pond.
She watches them while they nap in the sun.
     Only a few will survive.

This old gator lumbers along like a log on legs:
left back leg and right front leg forward;
then back right leg and left front leg.

He's king of the road.

Loggerhead Sea Turtle

At daybreak,
    all you can see
    are tracks in the sand.
    Parallel trenches
    coming up from the ocean,
    then going back down again.
At starlight,
    you don't see the
    loggerhead sea turtle
    pull her heavy body
        slowly   slowly
    up the beach,
    until she finds the spot,
    near where she was born,
    and her mother, too.

She digs and she digs, scooping out sand to make a large hole.

Finally, she stops.

Her leathery eggs,
  dozens and dozens
  of them,
come out of her
  plop
    plop
      plop.
Her eyes leak tears—
  of pain?
  of glory?
  of regret?
She crawls back
  to the water.
    Done.

Fox Squirrel

Have you ever seen
a *black squirrel?*
He sits atop
a branch and twirls
his foxy tail,
his mind awhirl
with visions of acorns
and nuts—his pearls.

The *anole* has a little trick.
If something tries
to catch him—
Quick!
(a cat or dog
or bird of prey)—
he runs along
his merry way
but leaves his tail behind!

This little lizard's
green or brown
depending on
the mood or scene,
running
here   or   there.

At last he finds
    a mate to pair with.

His throat becomes
    a red balloon
that pulses with
    his soundless croon.

She lets him find her.

Anole

Brown eyes glistening,
cocked heads listening,
pointed noses twitching—

at the slightest of sounds,
or dimmest of sights,
or faintest of scents—

they leap and bound
in furious flight
so quickly you'd think
them a vision you'd dreamt.

White-tailed deer

This one,
fearless,
all alone,
charges out into danger:
out of the night,
into the day.

The *dolphin*'s brain is half awake; the other half's asleep.
The waked half knows that she must breathe and calls her from the deep.
Her blow hole nose exchanges air and   now she's ready to prepare
to jump and twirl and leap.

Awake or asleep—real or a dream—
how can she tell the difference between?

The mother *dolphin* folds in half and **MMMM**s the water with her calf who swims alongside easily in mother's slipstream wake.
They glide through water smooth as silk and baby pulls on mother's milk.

And then there's you, you human,
   another Lowcountry critter.
Just because you're tall and smart—
You think only *you* have a heart.
Can't you hear the beats
   all around you?

These critters aren't performing just for you.
They don't need, they don't heed your grand applause,
your oohs and ahs, for their winged beauty, their stilled faces,
their countless colors, their muscular graces.

They are, like you,
mundane miracles.

Located midway between Beaufort and Bluffton, South Carolina, Callawassie Island is a golf and tennis community devoted to preserving its unique environment in the Lowcountry. Surrounded by salt marshes, the island boasts forests of live oaks, pines, palmettos, and magnolias. Many species of birds, from bluebirds to bald eagles, nest on the island, and numerous animals such as alligators, deer, foxes, and snakes make their home here. Spartina grass growing in the marshes provides a nutrient-rich breeding ground for shrimp and oysters, which feed the many water creatures. In 2006, Callawassie Island became the first community in South Carolina to be certified by the National Wildlife Federation as a Community Wildlife Habitat, and many Island members maintain their status as keepers of Backyard Wildlife Habitats. Additionally, due to the ecologically safe practices of fertilization and irrigation, the golf course has been certified by the Audubon Society.

Archeological digs at the Callawassie Burial Mound have revealed artifacts of an ancient settlement at least 4000 years old, and other remains have been identified as part of the Yemassee Indian culture. English settlers arrived in 1711, and ruins from their structures still are in evidence. Of particular note are the tabby (oyster-shell concrete) ruins of the Callawassie Sugar Works, listed on the National Register of Historic Places. Ownership of the Island is complicated: a succession of English landlords and American plantation owners relied on enslaved people to produce cash crops of indigo, cotton, and sugar cane. After the Civil War, mainly tenant farmers occupied the Island, enduring the devastating hurricanes, diseases, floods, and earthquakes to raise cattle and corn, or to be used as hunting grounds, until corporate entrepreneurs tried and failed at various schemes for exploitation. Not until the 1980s was the Island sold and begun to be developed into the community that it is today.

All photos are by Nancy Sinick except for the following: pages 32-34 and the back cover are by Carlos Chacon of the Coastal Discovery Museum of Hilton Head Island; page 10 is by Richard Henry of Callawassie Island; the hat on page 8 and the butterfly egg on page 17 are stock photos. Many thanks to Ben and Birdie Jo Lee for posing on page 42. Both Anita Tarr and Nancy Sinick live on Callawassie Island. All profits go to the Friends of Callawassie Island, Inc., charity organization, which gives generously to those in need in Beaufort and Jasper counties.

Made in the USA
Columbia, SC
02 December 2020

25959352R00027